This book belongs to

....

....

....

Copyright © Macmillan Publishers International Ltd 2016
Published in the United States by Kingfisher,
175 Fifth Ave., New York, NY 10010
Kingfisher is an imprint of Macmillan Children's Books, London
All rights reserved.

Distributed in the U.S. and Canada by Macmillan,
175 Fifth Ave., New York, NY 10010

Library of Congress Cataloging-in-Publication data
has been applied for.

Design by Fiona Hajée
Text by Erin Chamberlain, adapted from an original text by Trevor Barnes

ISBN 978-0-7534-4185-5

Kingfisher books are available for special promotions
and premiums. For details contact: Special Markets
Department, Macmillan, 175 Fifth Ave.,
New York, NY 10010.

For more information, please visit
www.kingfisherbooks.com

Printed in China

9 8 7 6 5 4 3 2 1
1TR/0117/MCI/UG/128MA

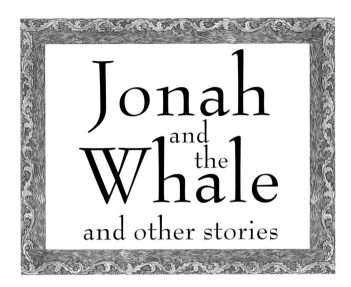

Jonah and the Whale

and other stories

KINGFISHER
NEW YORK

Jonah and the Whale

Jonah

One day God spoke to the prophet Jonah. "Go to Nineveh and tell the people there to change their evil ways." Jonah did not want to go. He was angry that God would give wicked people a second chance. But God loved them.

Jonah disobeyed God and he got on a ship sailing away from Nineveh.

A violent storm hit the ship. The crew were terrified and prayed to their gods to save them.

Jonah knew the storm was his fault. He said, "This storm has been sent to punish me for disobeying the Lord. Throw me in the sea and the storm will stop."

The sailors threw Jonah over the side of the ship, and the waters grew calm. Jonah was sure that he was going to drown, but at God's command a whale rose from the ocean and swallowed him alive.

For three days Jonah survived in the whale's belly, praying to God. At last the Lord came to his rescue and commanded the whale to spit him out onto the beach.

Safe on dry land, Jonah set off
for Nineveh, where he announced
that in forty days the city would
be destroyed.

For once the people listened.
They turned their backs on their
evil ways and worshiped God.
Seeing this God spared them.

⟡ The End ⟡

Elijah and the Ravens

1 Kings 16:29–17:24

King Ahab and his Canaanite wife, Jezabel, did more to anger God than any king before. They turned away from God and built a temple to Baal, a Canaanite god.

God sent prophets to tell Ahab he was not pleased with him. Elijah was one of these prophets. One day he went to King Ahab to warn him of a terrible drought.

"I speak in the name of the one true God," said Elijah. "There will be neither rain nor dew on this land for the next few years. Until I say so, not a drop of water will fall."

God said to Elijah, "Now leave. Go east, beyond the Jordan River, to the Brook of Cherith. For now the brook will supply you with water, and I have commanded ravens to bring you food."

Elijah did as the Lord had commanded. Each morning and night ravens came, carrying scraps of bread and meat in their beaks. But in time, the brook dried up because of the lack of rain.

God told Elijah to go to the town of Zarephath, near Sidon. He met a woman at the gate of the town and asked her for some water and some bread.

She said to him, "I swear by the Lord Almighty, all I have is a handful of flour and a little olive oil. I will cook this last meal for my son and me. After this we will starve. "Do not worry,"

said Elijah. "If you look after me
the Lord, the God of Israel, will
not let you run out of flour or oil
until there is rain."

⊰ The End ⊱

Exile

2 Kings 22–23; 25–26; Jeremiah, Ezekiel

The kings and people of God turned their back on him and worshiped the moon and the stars. They performed all kinds of witchcraft and magic, and practiced human sacrifice.

The prophets still came to warn the people that if they continued to disobey God they would be destroyed—but the people refused to listen. At last, through the prophets, God said, "I will abandon the people and hand them over to their enemies."

Soon the armies of Babylonia, under King Nebuchadnezzar, were marching into Jerusalem.

Within months the enemy had captured and plundered the city. They took the royal family into captivity and

deported eight thousand men of fighting
age to Babylonia, never to see their
homeland again.

They looted the Temple and set it on fire. They took all the gold and silver to Babylonia. Houses were burned and people were killed where they stood. This was the price of disobedience to God.

As God had warned, Jerusalem had fallen, and the exile to Babylonia had begun.

But all was not lost. God had
made a promise that all
people on the Earth would
be blessed through Israel.

Through the prophet Ezekiel, God sent an amazing message. Ezekiel saw a valley full of skeletons. "Tell my people they are like these bones," said God. "They think they are withering in exile without any hope. But if they follow my laws, I will breathe new life into them."

The End

lions' den themselves and torn limb from limb.

Darius passed another law. "By the decree of Darius," it read, "the whole kingdom will respect the God of Daniel. He is the living God, and he lives for ever."

−§ *The End* §−

"Your Majesty, God sent an angel to stop the lions from harming me. God knew I was innocent and that I had done you no wrong," answered Daniel.

The king was overjoyed and commanded that Daniel be removed from the lions' den. Everyone saw there was not a single scratch on him. Daniel's accusers were not so lucky. They were thrown into the

"I hope the God you serve will rescue you," Darius said. Daniel was taken to the lions' den and a boulder was rolled over the entrance.

That night the king could not sleep. As soon as the sun rose, he ran to the lions' den and shouted, "Daniel, was your God able to protect you from the lions?"

changed. At sunset he reluctantly ordered that Daniel be brought out and thrown into a pit of lions.

Daniel heard about the law, but when he went to his rooms, he prayed in front of his windows as usual. His enemies saw him. Immediately they went to the king and accused him of breaking the new law.

The king was very upset at the thought of losing Daniel, and he spent all day trying to find a way to save him. But his law could not be

"Let's use his religion against him," they decided.

It was well known that Daniel served the Lord and he prayed each day. His enemies convinced King Darius to make a new law. It would be illegal to ask for anything from any god or man except the king. Those breaking the law should be thrown to the lions.

Daniel in the Lions' Den

Daniel 6:1–26

King Darius put Daniel in charge of all the administrators. They were jealous and tried to give Daniel a bad name. But this was impossible, because he was faithful to the king.

Daniel said, "This is a warning from my God. The words written here are 'MENE, MENE, TEKEL, UPHARSIN.' They mean that God will destroy your kingdom."

That night, the Persians invaded the kingdom. Belshazzar was killed and Darius the Mede became king.

The End

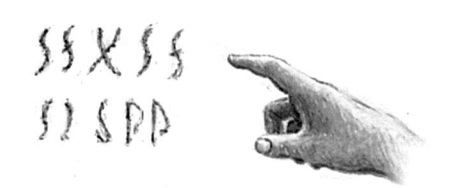

Suddenly a human hand appeared from thin air and began to write four strange words on the wall. Then it disappeared.

No one could explain the meaning of the words. Belshazzar sent for Daniel.

in gold and silver goblets that
had been taken from the Temple
in Jerusalem, where they had
been used for the worship of God.
Belshazzar and his guests used
them to drink to their own gods.

Daniel and the Writing on the Wall

Daniel 5

Nebuchadnezzar died, and his son, Belshazzar, became king of Babylonia. One evening he organized a great banquet for one thousand of his noblemen. He served them wine

Nebuchadnezzar looked into the fiery furnace, and saw a fourth figure beside the three men. "It looks like an angel. Let them out!" he said.

When the three men came out, they were completely well. Nebuchadnezzar was amazed and commanded everyone to praise and respect the Lord God.

The End

heard of their disobedience, he was angry. "Very well," he said. "You know what the penalty is."

He ordered the furnace to be heated to seven times hotter than usual and had the three men thrown in. The heat of the furnace killed the soldiers who took them there.

As soon as the trumpets sounded, the king ordered everyone to bow down to the statue. Anyone who refused would be thrown into a blazing furnace and burned to death.

As the fanfare sounded everyone knelt, except for Shadrach, Meshach, and Abednego. When the king

Abednego, were all from noble families in Judah. They were well treated and exceled at all that they did. They soon became valued advisors at the court.

Nebuchadnezzar built a huge golden statue to one of his own gods. It was unveiled in front of all the important people in the land— but Daniel was not there.

The Fiery Furnace

Daniel 1–4

Daniel was a young man when King Nebuchadnezzar attacked Jerusalem. He was taken into captivity with other young men from the richest families. Daniel and his three friends, Shadrach, Meshach, and

Daniel
and the
Lions
and other stories

KINGFISHER
NEW YORK

Bible References

This book belongs to

....

....

....

Copyright © Macmillan Publishers International Ltd 2016
Published in the United States by Kingfisher,
175 Fifth Ave., New York, NY 10010
Kingfisher is an imprint of Macmillan Children's Books, London
All rights reserved.

Distributed in the U.S. and Canada by Macmillan,
175 Fifth Ave., New York, NY 10010

Library of Congress Cataloging-in-Publication data
has been applied for.

Design by Fiona Hajée
Text by Erin Chamberlain, adapted from an original text by Trevor Barnes

ISBN 978-0-7534-4184-8

Kingfisher books are available for special promotions
and premiums. For details contact: Special Markets
Department, Macmillan, 175 Fifth Ave.,
New York, NY 10010.

For more information, please visit
www.kingfisherbooks.com

Printed in China

9 8 7 6 5 4 3 2 1
1TR/0117/MCI/UG/128MA

Moses
in the
Reeds
and other stories

KINGFISHER
NEW YORK

Moses in the Reeds

Exodus 2:1–10

After Joseph died, the Israelites grew in number in Egypt. A new Pharaoh came to power, took their

possessions, and made them slaves.

Still the number of Israelites grew. The Pharaoh issued a command: "Every newborn Israelite boy is to be thrown into the River Nile and drowned at birth."

An Israelite couple with two children, Aaron and Miriam, had a third child—a boy. They were frightened of Pharaoh's command.

The mother hid her baby.
Then she made a basket out of
reeds and placed her baby inside.
She put the basket in the reeds at
the edge of the River Nile, and
told Miriam to keep watch.

Pharaoh's daughter came to
the river with her maids to bathe.
Seeing the basket, she sent a maid
to fetch it.

They lifted the lid and saw a tiny baby crying. "This is one of the Israelite children," said Pharaoh's daughter.

Suddenly she heard a voice. It was Miriam.

"Should I find an Israelite nursemaid to look after him for you?" she asked.

"Yes," said Pharaoh's daughter,

who had no children of her own.
So Miriam went away and returned
with her mother.

"Take this child away, and look
after him for me. I will pay you
to be his nurse," said Pharaoh's
daughter.

So the child was brought up in
the royal palace as an Egyptian
prince. And he was named Moses.

The End

Moses and the Burning Bush

Exodus 2:11–25; 3; 4:1–17

Moses was brought up as an Egyptian, but he knew he was an Israelite. It made him angry to see his people being treated so badly. One day, he

attacked and killed an Egyptian
slave master.

Pharaoh commanded that Moses
be killed. So, Moses ran far away to
the land of Midian. He lived there
for many years and got married.
Meanwhile the suffering of the
Israelites grew worse and they
cried out to God, who remembered
his promises to Abraham, Isaac,
and Jacob.

Later, Moses was watching sheep
on Mount Sinai when he saw
something strange. A bush was on

fire, but it did not burn up. As
Moses went closer to look, the voice
of God called out to him from the
burning bush.

"Do not come nearer. Take off your sandals, you are on holy ground. I am the Lord, your God."

Moses hid his face, because he was afraid.

God spoke again. "I have seen how badly my people are being treated in Egypt, and I have come to set them free. Go and tell Pharaoh."

Moses didn't think he was important or powerful enough. God said, "I will be with you."

"Please send someone else, Lord," he pleaded.

"No!" said God angrily. "Your brother Aaron will be with you. I will tell you what to do. Trust me, and I will give you the strength."

The End

The Plagues of Egypt

Exodus 4:18–31; 5–10

Moses returned to Egypt. God told Moses that he would harden the Pharaoh's heart and make him stubborn so that at first he would refuse to let the people go. Moses and Aaron went to the court of the Pharaoh and spoke with him. "This is what the Lord God commands," they said. "You must let the Israelites go, so they can travel into the desert to worship God."

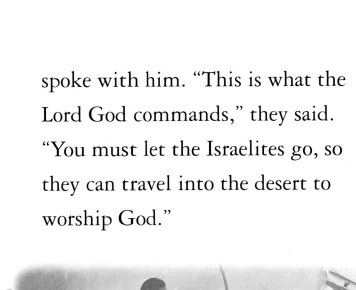

But Pharaoh refused to let the
Israelites go. So, God gave Pharaoh
ten warnings, called "Plagues."
First, God turned the River Nile
into blood. All the fish died, and
there was no drinking water.

Next, God unleashed a plague of
frogs. Pharaoh begged Moses to ask
God to remove the frogs. No sooner
had the frogs disappeared, Pharaoh
hardened his heart and again refused
to let the Israelites go.

Then God sent millions of gnats. They infested all the people and animals of Egypt. But still Pharaoh did not budge.

God sent a swarm of flies that covered the whole of Egypt. Pharaoh pleaded for the flies to be sent away. The next day the flies were gone, but Pharaoh was as stubborn as ever. After that, God sent a terrible disease that killed

all of the animals, then a plague of
boils—terrible sores that covered
the bodies of the Egyptians.

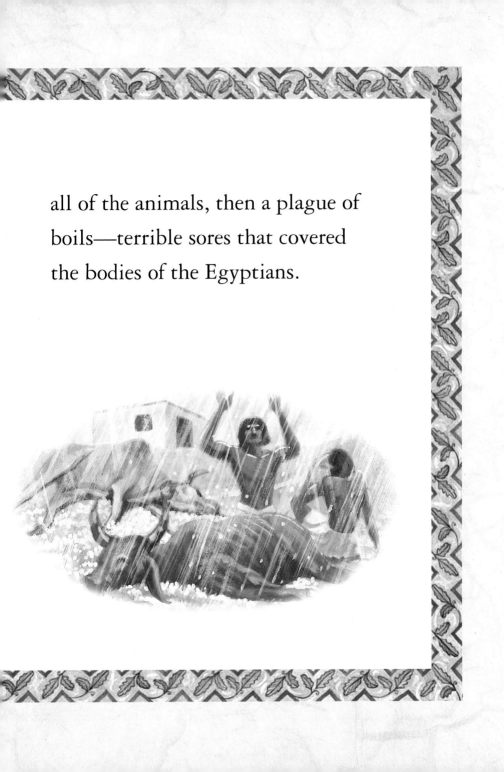

Even when hailstones and locusts
destroyed all the crops and plants,
Pharaoh's heart remained hard.

God told Moses to stretch out
his hand toward Heaven and bring

darkness to cover Egypt. For three days, the country was in darkness. After this, Pharaoh said that the Israelites could go—but leave their animals. This was unacceptable to Moses. "Then you will stay," said Pharaoh to Moses in fury.

The last plague was the most terrible. Moses told Pharaoh God's words.

"If you do not let my people go, every firstborn Egyptian boy will perish." But still Pharaoh refused.

God told the Israelites to kill their best lambs and smear blood around the doors of their houses. This was a sign to God, so He would pass over their houses and spare their children.

It happened, just as God said. There was great sorrow across

Egypt. Immediately Pharaoh summoned Moses. "Be gone!" he cried. "Take your people and go!"

⸲ The End ⸲

The Israelites destroyed Jericho, and Joshua was famous throughout Canaan.

The End

of the Ark. On the seventh day walk around the city seven times, and when you hear a long blast on the horns, shout loudly and the walls of the city will come tumbling down."

Joshua and the Israelites did these things. On the seventh day they marched around the city seven times. The priests sounded the horns and the people let out a great cry—and the walls of Jericho fell to the ground.

The spies returned and Joshua readied the army. The priests went first with the Ark of the Covenant. The Jordan River was flooded but when the priests took the Ark into the water, a dry pathway formed and the army crossed in safety.

The gates of Jericho were shut against them. God said to Joshua, "Jericho is yours. For six days march the army around the city. Seven priests carrying trumpets must walk in front the people across the Jordan River into the Promised Land.

Joshua sent spies into the land to Jericho to check out its defenses. To avoid detection, they spent the night at the house of a woman called Rahab. She hid them and arranged for them to escape over the city wall. In return, the spies promised to save the lives of Rahab and her family.

The Walls of Jericho

Joshua 1–6

God's people traveled for forty years in the desert. During this time, Moses died, and Joshua became the leader of the Israelites. God told Joshua to lead

have gold carrying rings attached
to it.

When the Ark of the Covenant
and the Tent of the Lord's Presence
were finished, a cloud settled over
them, and a dazzling light showed the
Israelites that the Lord was present.
The sacred tent was a reminder of
God's presence with them.

The End

The Ark was to be built to house
the tablets of stone on which the Law,
the Ten Commandments, had been
written. It was to be made of
acacia wood, covered with gold, and

sanctuary—a sacred place—for me to live among them."

The Lord gave them precise instructions. They were to build a special tent, the Tabernacle, which would contain the Lord's presence. The tent would be a holy place, and the part of the tent where the ceremonial box, or the Ark, stood would be extra special, the Holy of Holies.

The Ark of
the Covenant

Exodus 25–30

Again God spoke to Moses
and said, "Tell the
Israelites to make offerings of gold,
silver, and other precious items.
With these they are to make a

The Israelites saw smoke and lightning on the mountain and were afraid. Moses explained that God was testing their obedience. He told them the Ten Commandments, and the Israelites promised to obey them forever. The commandments were written on two tablets of stone.

⊱ *The End* ⊰

Sabbath, and keep it holy. Rest on the seventh.

"Respect your father and mother.

"Do not commit murder.

"Do not commit adultery.

"Do not steal.

"Do not tell lies.

"Do not envy your neighbor's things."

At the appointed time, God called Moses up the mountain and gave him the ten commandments.

God said, "I am the Lord, who brought you out of slavery. Worship no other god but me.

"Do not bow down to false idols.

"Use my name with respect.

"Remember the seventh day, the

there he heard the voice of God
speaking to him.

"Remind the Israelites," God
said, "of how I brought them
here safely. Remind them of my
promises to them and tell them, if
they obey me, they will continue to
be my special people and grow into
a holy nation."

The Ten Commandments

Exodus 19–20

Three months after leaving Egypt, the Israelites pitched camp at the foot of Mount Sinai. Leaving the people below, Moses climbed the mountain, and

The Ten
Commandments
and other stories

KINGFISHER
NEW YORK

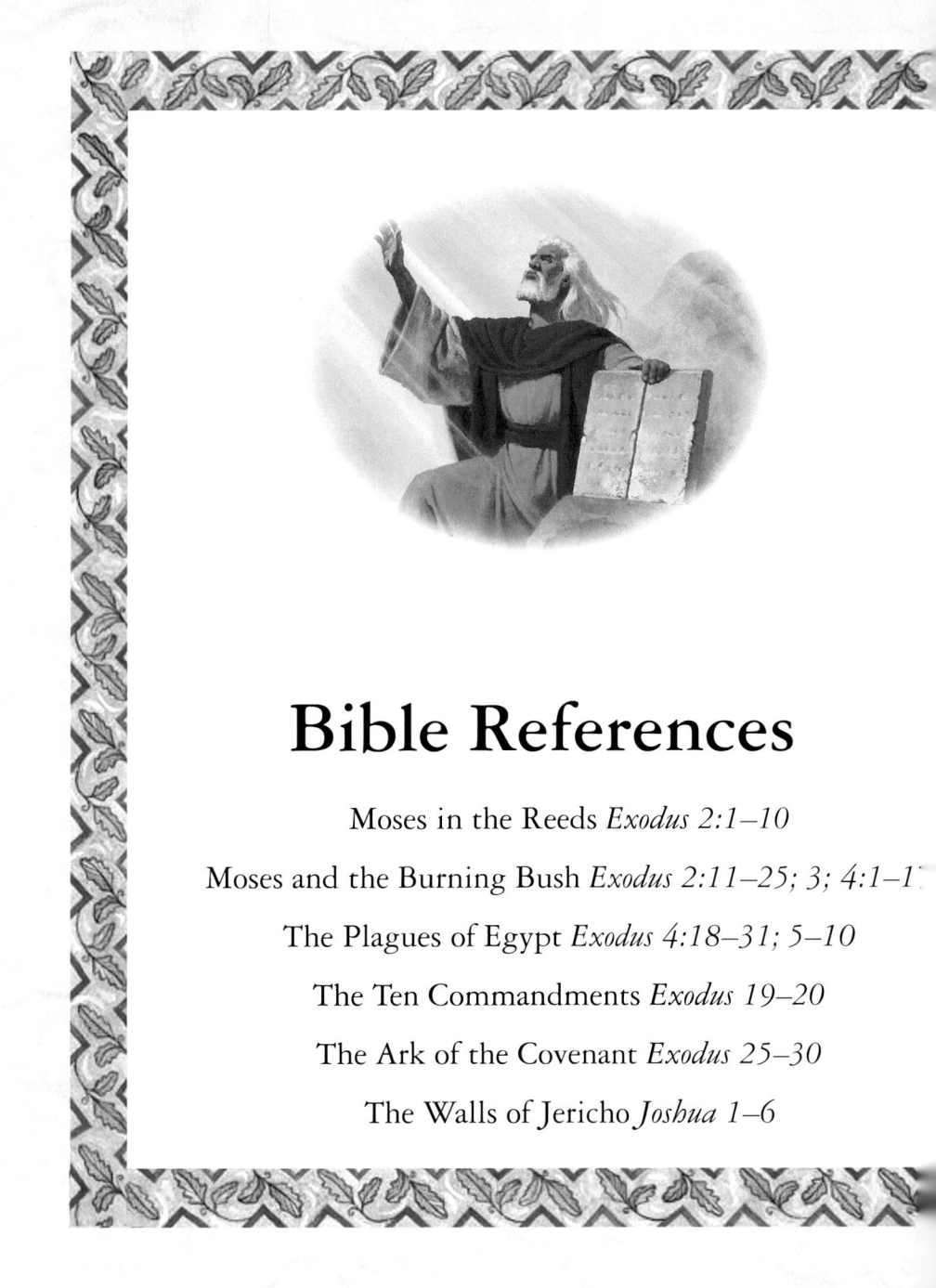

Bible References

This book belongs to

....

....

....

Copyright © Macmillan Publishers International Ltd 2016
Published in the United States by Kingfisher,
175 Fifth Ave., New York, NY 10010
Kingfisher is an imprint of Macmillan Children's Books, London
All rights reserved.

Distributed in the U.S. and Canada by Macmillan,
175 Fifth Ave., New York, NY 10010

Library of Congress Cataloging-in-Publication data
has been applied for.

Design by Fiona Hajée
Text by Erin Chamberlain, adapted from an original text by Trevor Barnes

ISBN 978-0-7534-4183-1

Kingfisher books are available for special promotions
and premiums. For details contact: Special Markets
Department, Macmillan, 175 Fifth Ave.,
New York, NY 10010.

For more information, please visit
www.kingfisherbooks.com

Printed in China

9 8 7 6 5 4 3 2 1
1TR/0117/MCI/UG/128MA

Adam
and Eve
and other stories

KINGFISHER
NEW YORK

In the Beginning

Genesis 1:1–2:3

In the beginning God made the universe. At first everything was dark, and raging waters covered the Earth. The power of God gave the world a shape. "Let there be light!" said God. And there was light.

On the first day of creation God separated the light from the darkness to make Day and Night.

On the second day God said: "Let there be a dome above the waters, and let it be called Heaven." And so the sky appeared.

On the third day God created the dry land and filled the oceans with water.

On the fourth day God
commanded lights to appear in the
sky. The sun was to rule the day, and
the moon and stars to rule the night.

On the fifth day God filled
the oceans and skies with animals.
Whales and fish swam in the ocean,
and colorful birds flew above.

On the sixth day God ordered
the Earth to produce every kind of
animal—from the largest elephant
to the smallest mouse. God was
pleased. "It is time to make human
beings. They will have a part of me
in them."

God made some humans male
and some humans female, and
blessed them all. "Be fruitful and
multiply. I am putting you in

charge of all creatures. The plants will be your food."

On the sixth day the universe was finished. On the seventh day God rested. From that time on, the seventh day was set aside as a day of rest—a holy day to mark the creation of the world.

The End

Adam and Eve

Genesis 2:4–3:24

When God first made the Earth, nothing grew there. The seeds did not sprout because there was no one to look after them. Then a mist appeared, and later rain, and the seeds grew. God made the first man out of dust.

God planted a beautiful garden
in a place called Eden. Cool shady
trees, pretty flowers, and delicious
fruits grew there. In the middle
stood two trees: the Tree of Life
and the Tree of Knowledge of Good
and Evil.

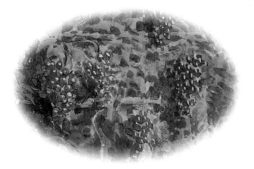

God led the man, called Adam, into the Garden of Eden. "You can eat whatever you like," said God, "but if you eat from the Tree of Knowledge you will die."

Adam looked after the garden, but he grew lonely. God had made many animals to live in the garden with Adam, but he needed a true friend.

While Adam slept, God removed a rib from his body and made it into a woman. Her name was Eve. When Adam woke up and saw her, he said, "Here is a creature of my kind, made of flesh, blood, and bone like me." Adam and Eve walked naked in the garden. Neither felt any shame or embarrassment.

The End

Leaving the Garden

Genesis 2:4–3:24

O f all God's animals, the snake was the slyest. It slid up to Eve. "Did God really tell you not to eat from certain trees?"

"We can eat from all the trees except the tree in the middle of the garden," Eve replied. "If we do that, we will certainly die."

"No, no, you will not die," said the snake. "As soon as you eat from it, you will be given great powers. You will understand Good and Evil and be like God."

Eve thought it would be marvelous to be like God. Eve picked a fruit and ate it. Then Adam ate the fruit too.

As soon as they had eaten the fruit, something changed. For the first time Adam and Eve saw they were naked, and they quickly sewed fig leaves together to cover themselves.

When they heard God, they hid among the trees.

"Where are you?" called God.

"I am here," replied Adam. "I was afraid because I was naked. So I hid."

"Who told you that you were naked?" asked God. "Have you eaten from the tree that I told you not to touch?"

"The woman offered me some of its fruit, and I ate it," replied Adam.

God turned to Eve. "Why did you do such a thing?"

"The snake tricked me," said Eve.

God said to the snake, "You will be punished. You will crawl on your belly forevermore and eat dust."

And God said to Adam and Eve, "Now that you have knowledge of

Good and Evil, you cannot remain in Eden."

God clothed Adam and Eve and sent them out of the garden into the world beyond.

❧ *The End* ☙

The next morning, he
dedicated the place to God.

⊰ *The End* ⊱

He dreamed of a stairway stretching from the Earth to Heaven, with angels going up and down. God was at the top and he said, "I am the God of Abraham and of Isaac." God told Jacob that he would look after him and that he would receive the promises given to Abraham.

Jacob woke up, afraid. He felt God's presence all around him.

and that all people would be blessed through him.

Jacob tricked his brother Esau out of receiving the inheritance and blessing from Isaac. He then ran away to Mesopotamia, where his father had told him to find a wife. He traveled all day and when night came, he stopped to sleep, using a stone as a pillow. That night he had a strange dream.

Jacob's Dream

Genesis 28

Jacob was the son of Isaac, who was the son of Abraham, the very first Israelite. God made great promises to Abraham. He promised a country to live in, many children, blessings,

Babylonia all over the Earth.

That is why the tower is called the Tower of Babel—because God confused the speech of the whole world into a "babble" of different languages and tore them apart forever.

⊹ *The End* ⊹

God came down to see the city and the tower. He wasn't pleased. "If this is what people speaking the same language can do," he said, "nothing they plan to do will be impossible for them."

So God confused their speech. The people spoke different languages and were not able to understand each other any more. God scattered them from

Then they said, "Let's build ourselves a city with a gigantic tower that reaches all the way up to Heaven. We will be famous. We'll be like God himself."

They said to each other, "Let us make bricks out of clay and bake them." They stuck the bricks together with tar for mortar and built towns and fortresses. They were very proud of themselves.

Tower of Babel

Genesis 11:1–9

Noah's sons had many children, and their children had children too. The world was filled with people who all spoke the same language. Some of them moved from the east and made their home in Babylonia.

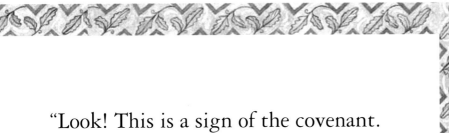

"Look! This is a sign of the covenant. Every time I see a rainbow, I will remember my promise."

The End

The first thing Noah did was to build an altar and give thanks to God. God was very pleased and blessed Noah and his family, saying, "Be fruitful and multiply and fill the Earth again."

Then God said, "Never again will I destroy the Earth. This promise is for you, and for every future generation." A rainbow appeared in the sky and God said,

When Noah sent out a dove
to see if the water had gone down,
it finally came back with an olive
branch in its beak. Noah knew the
waters had subsided.

God told Noah to leave the ark
with his family and the animals,
so that they could start to
repopulate the Earth.

Noah and his family and all
the animals were safe inside the ark.
When the rain stopped, the ark
came to rest on top of Mount Ararat.

Soon, just as God had promised, the rain fell in torrents. As the waters rose, the ground was submerged.

For forty days and forty nights rain fell on the Earth. Soon the water covered the highest mountains. Everything drowned beneath the waves, except Noah's ark, which floated with its precious cargo on the ocean.

"Gather together two of every kind of animal and load them into the boat. Then climb aboard with your family. I will send rain to flood the Earth. Everything will be destroyed except for your family and the animals."

The animals went into the boat two by two, male and female, side by side.

everything—men, women, animals, and birds."

God made one exception, and his name was Noah. He was a good man who did all that God commanded.

God said to Noah, "You and your family will be saved. I will make a covenant—a firm agreement—with you. Build a huge boat, called an ark, with many rooms."

Noah's Ark

Genesis 6–7; 8; 9:1–17

Many years passed, and the number of people on the Earth increased. But the people were now so wicked that God began to regret having created them.

So God said, "I have created the world. Now I will destroy

Noah's Ark
and other stories

KINGFISHER
NEW YORK

Bible References

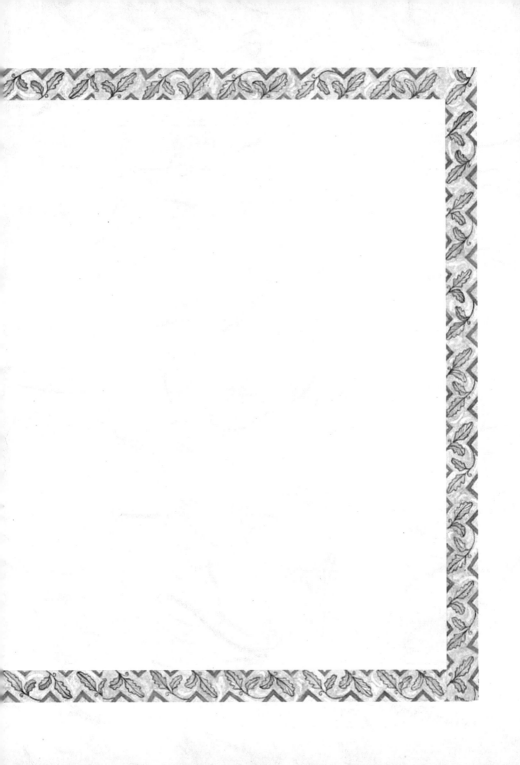

This book belongs to

....

....

....

Distributed in the U.S. and Canada by Macmillan,
175 Fifth Ave., New York, NY 10010

Library of Congress Cataloging-in-Publication data
has been applied for.

Design by Fiona Hajée
Text by Erin Chamberlain, adapted from an original text by Trevor Barnes

ISBN 978-0-7534-4186-2

Kingfisher books are available for special promotions
and premiums. For details contact: Special Markets
Department, Macmillan, 175 Fifth Ave.,
New York, NY 10010.

For more information, please visit
www.kingfisherbooks.com

Printed in China

9 8 7 6 5 4 3 2 1
1TR/0117/MCI/UG/128MA

Joseph's Coat
of Many
Colors
and other stories

KINGFISHER
NEW YORK

Joseph and
his Brothers

Genesis 37

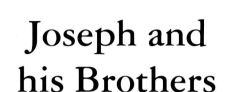

Jacob had twelve sons. Of all
his sons, Joseph was his
favorite. To show his love, Jacob
made him a fine woven coat with
threads of many colors. But the
special attention Joseph received

made his brothers hate him.

One night Joseph had a dream.
When he told it to his brothers,
it made them hate him even more.

"We were all in the field tying
up sheaves of wheat," he said,
"when my sheaf suddenly stood up
straight. Then your sheaves formed
a circle around it and bowed down
to it."

"So you think that means you are better than we are, do you?" they sneered.

A while later Joseph had another dream in which he saw the sun, the moon, and the stars bowing down to him. This time he told it to his father as well as to his brothers.

Jacob was angry. "What is this dream of yours supposed to mean?" he asked. "Do you expect all the family to bow down before you?" All the same, Jacob could not get the dream out of his mind. But Joseph's brothers despised him all the more.

One day Jacob asked Joseph to go to the fields and check his brothers and the sheep were safe. His brothers saw him coming and they made plans to kill him.

"Here comes the dreamer," they said. "Let's kill him and drop his body into a pit. We can say that he was eaten by a wild animal."

His brother Reuben tried to protect Joseph from them. "No, let's not kill him," he said. "Let's just leave him in a pit in the desert." Reuben hoped to be able to rescue Joseph later.

The brothers took the coat
and threw Joseph into a dry well.
A group of merchants came along
and they decided to sell him for
twenty pieces of silver. Joseph was
taken to Egypt.

The brothers dipped the coat
in blood and took it back to their
father. Jacob believed Joseph
had died.

The End

Joseph and Pharaoh

Genesis 41–49

Joseph was sold to Potiphar, one of Pharaoh's officials. Joseph did well and was put in charge of the whole household. However, Joseph rejected the advances of Potiphar's wife; she accused him falsely, and

Joseph was thrown in jail.

God took care of Joseph. Joseph was put in charge of running the jail. One day, Pharaoh's personal wine taster and his chief baker were jailed. Joseph noticed that they were both very upset and he asked them why.

"Our dreams trouble us," said one, "and no one can tell us what they mean."

The men told Joseph their dreams. With God's help, Joseph told them what they meant and it came to pass.

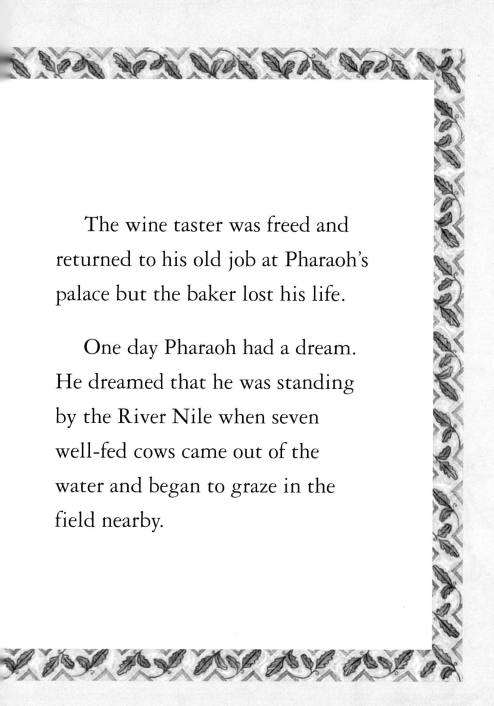

The wine taster was freed and returned to his old job at Pharaoh's palace but the baker lost his life.

One day Pharaoh had a dream. He dreamed that he was standing by the River Nile when seven well-fed cows came out of the water and began to graze in the field nearby.

Then seven more cows, horribly thin and bony, came up out of the river. A strange thing happened—

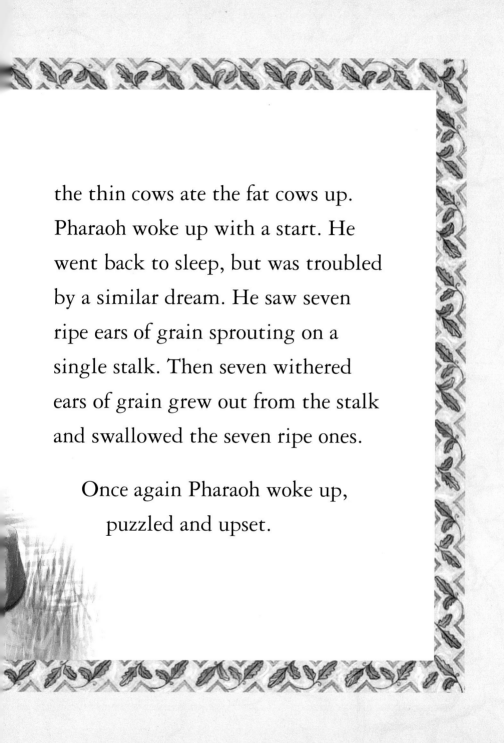

the thin cows ate the fat cows up.
Pharaoh woke up with a start. He
went back to sleep, but was troubled
by a similar dream. He saw seven
ripe ears of grain sprouting on a
single stalk. Then seven withered
ears of grain grew out from the stalk
and swallowed the seven ripe ones.

Once again Pharaoh woke up,
puzzled and upset.

Pharaoh sent for his advisors to discover what the dreams meant. The wine taster remembered Joseph. Pharaoh summoned him and told him his dreams.

With God's help, Joseph told Pharaoh what his dreams meant. "These two dreams mean the same thing. The cows and the grain represent years of plenty and famine. There will be seven years of

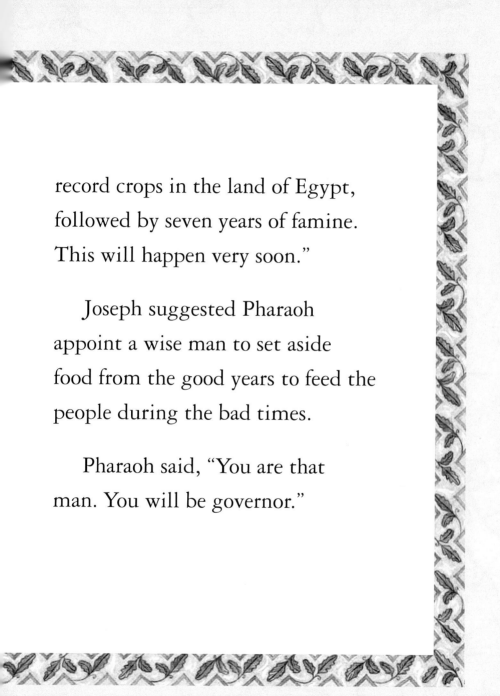

record crops in the land of Egypt,
followed by seven years of famine.
This will happen very soon."

Joseph suggested Pharaoh
appoint a wise man to set aside
food from the good years to feed the
people during the bad times.

Pharaoh said, "You are that
man. You will be governor."

In the years of famine, people came from many lands around to buy grain in Egypt. Even Joseph's family came, and it came to pass that his brothers did bow before him. God had planned for good all along—Joseph's family did not starve.

The End

Samson

Judges 13–16

The Israelites stopped obeying God. He allowed them to be defeated by their enemies. A special child, Samson, was born. An angel told his mother, "Don't ever cut your son's hair. One day he will rescue Israel from the Philistines."

As Samson grew, he became strong. He fell in love with a Philistine woman, named Delilah. The Philistine leaders offered her a bribe. "Find out the secret of Samson's strength," they said, "and we will give you lots of silver."

Delilah tried everything to uncover Samson's secret. She tied him up with seven new bowstrings and arranged for the Philistines to try to capture him. She tried to tie him with strong ropes. Each time Samson broke free and the men ran for their lives. Eventually Samson told her the truth.

"Ever since I was born, my hair

has never been cut. If someone were to cut it, I would be as weak as anyone."

That night, Delilah cut Samson's hair as he was sleeping. The Philistines captured him, blinded him, put him in chains, and made him a slave. All the while his hair was growing.

One day, Samson was called to a banquet. He asked the boy leading him to guide him between two pillars so that he could rest.

Samson took his revenge. He pushed the pillars and the building fell down. Samson killed more people with his own death than he had in his whole life.

The End

people together, and after the Ark of the Covenant had been placed, he prayed, "Praise the Lord of Israel and obey God's commands. Lord, hear us when we call to you. May we always be faithful to your word."

⋇ *The End* ⋇

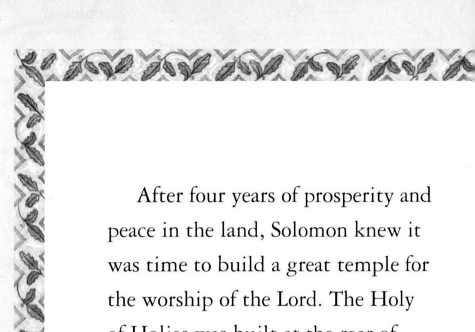

After four years of prosperity and peace in the land, Solomon knew it was time to build a great temple for the worship of the Lord. The Holy of Holies was built at the rear of the temple. It was the room where the Ark of the Covenant, the sacred vessel containing the laws of God, was to be placed.

After seven years the Temple was finished. Solomon gathered the

King Solomon's Temple

1 Kings 5–8

Solomon was King David's son. Shortly before he died, David gave Solomon his last instructions. "Be strong and keep the Lord's commandments," he said. "If you obey God, your reign will be blessed."

ceremonial tent. The crowds sang and
danced. This city was now not just
the capital. It was the city of God.

⌁ *The End* ⌁

Under David's rule, Israel
captured Jerusalem. A royal palace
was built there and David brought
the Ark of the Covenant into the
city where it was installed in the

was forced to live a life on the run, constantly fearing attack from Saul.

In time David heard news that Saul had been killed in battle.

After Saul's death, the northern tribes of Israel chose one of Saul's descendants to be their king, while the southern tribes chose David. Eventually David became king of all Israel.

David becomes King

1 Samuel 18–26; 2 Samuel 1–10

After defeating Goliath, David was very popular and became a national hero. This angered Saul and made him fear that David might be a rival. David

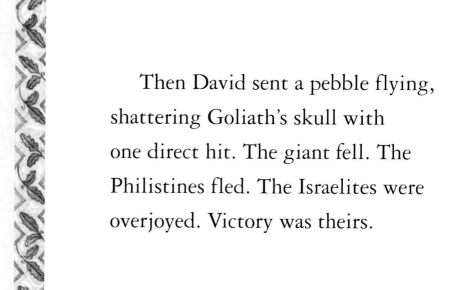

Then David sent a pebble flying, shattering Goliath's skull with one direct hit. The giant fell. The Philistines fled. The Israelites were overjoyed. Victory was theirs.

❦ *The End* ❧

that David was there and sent for
him. David said to Saul, "I will
fight Goliath. The Lord will help
me beat him!"

David picked up five pebbles
and, armed only with a slingshot
and a stick, he went to meet Goliath.

Goliath was not afraid. But David
said, "God is on my side, I have the
power to kill you. And I will."

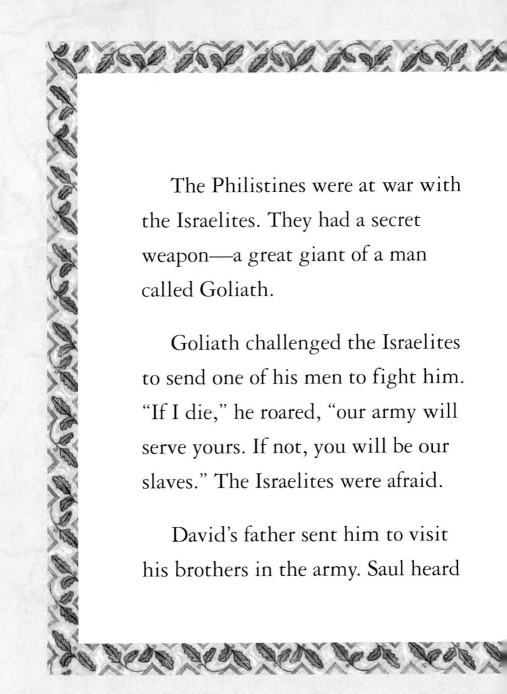

The Philistines were at war with the Israelites. They had a secret weapon—a great giant of a man called Goliath.

Goliath challenged the Israelites to send one of his men to fight him. "If I die," he roared, "our army will serve yours. If not, you will be our slaves." The Israelites were afraid.

David's father sent him to visit his brothers in the army. Saul heard

God sent Samuel to Bethlehem.
Samuel anointed Jesse's youngest
son, David, as the new king. David
was a shepherd—he protected his
flock with a slingshot.

David and Goliath

1 Samuel 8–17

God's people wanted a king. Saul was the first king of Israel. He was a good king, but he put his own desires above the wishes of God. Samuel, God's messenger, was told that God rejected Saul as the king and to choose a new one.

David
and
Goliath
and other stories

KINGFISHER
NEW YORK

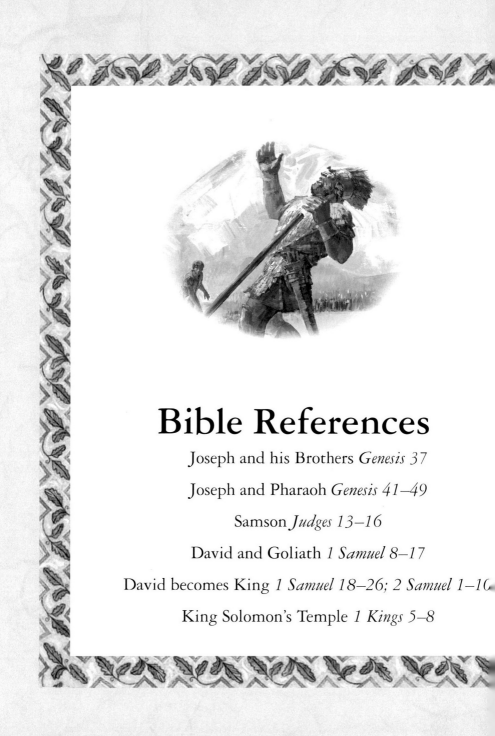

Bible References